EASIEST KEYBOARD COLLECTION

Sports Themes

WISE PUBLICATIONS
London/New York/Paris/Sydney/Copenhagen/Madrid

Exclusive Distributors:

Music Sales Limited
8/9 Frith Street,
London W1V 5TZ, England.

Music Sales Pty Limited
120 Rothschild Avenue,
Rosebery, NSW 2018,
Australia.

Order No. AM955801
ISBN 0-7119-7475-6
This book © Copyright 1999 by Wise Publications

Compiled by Nick Crispin
Music arranged by Roger Day
Music processed by Paul Ewers Music Design

Printed in the United Kingdom by
Caligraving Limited, Thetford, Norfolk.

Cover photograph courtesy of Superstock

Your Guarantee of Quality
As publishers, we strive to produce every book to the highest
commercial standards.
The music has been freshly engraved and the book has been carefully
designed to minimise awkward page turns and to make playing from
it a real pleasure.
Particular care has been given to specifying acid-free, neutral-sized
paper made from pulps which have not been elemental chlorine
bleached. This pulp is from farmed sustainable forests and was
produced with special regard for the environment.
Throughout, the printing and binding have been planned to ensure
a sturdy, attractive publication which should give years of enjoyment.
If your copy fails to meet our high standards, please inform us and
we will gladly replace it.

Music Sales' complete catalogue describes thousands of titles and is
available in full colour sections by subject, direct from Music Sales
Limited. Please state your areas of interest and send a cheque/postal
order for £1.50 for postage to: Music Sales Limited, Newmarket Road,
Bury St. Edmunds, Suffolk IP33 3YB.

www.internetmusicshop.com

Contents

A MUSICAL JOKE
(BBC Horse Of The Year Show)

Composed by Wolfgang Amadeus Mozart

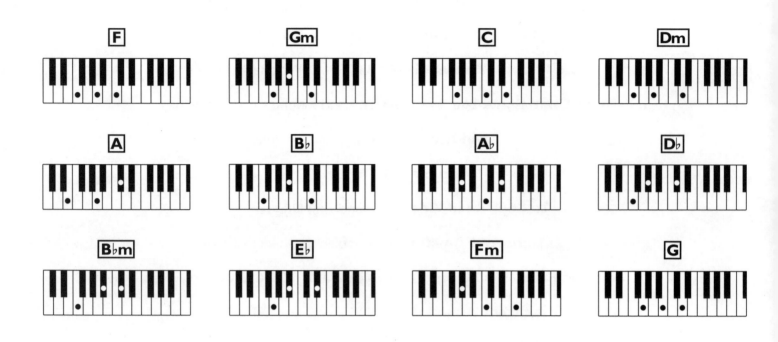

Voice: **Violin**

Rhythm: **Cumbia**

Tempo: ♩ = 98 135

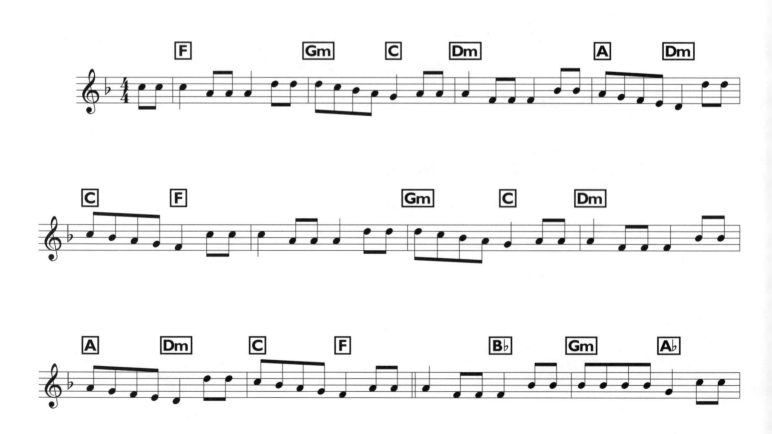

CARNAVAL DE PARIS
(World Cup '98)

By Paul Spencer, Stephen Spencer & Scott Rosser
© Copyright 1998 PolyGram Music Publishing Limited, 47 British Grove, London W4.
All Rights Reserved. International Copyright Secured.

Voice: **Trumpet**

Rhythm: **Samba**

Tempo: ♩ = 136

CHALLENGE
(BBC Sports Personality Of The Year)

By Charles Williams

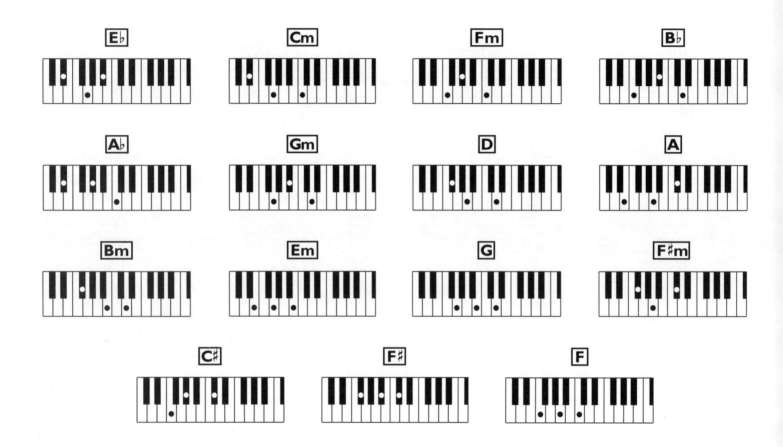

Voice: **Brass Ensemble**

Rhythm: **Serenade**

Tempo: ♩ = **96**

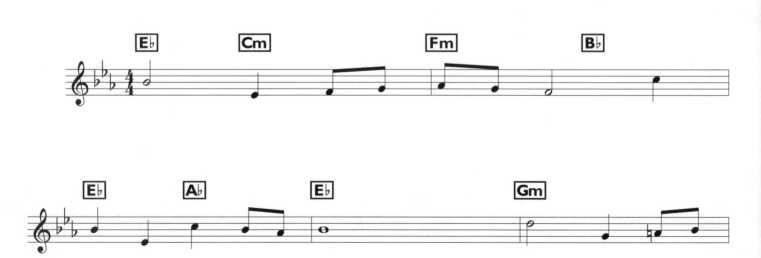

DON'T COME HOME TOO SOON
(Scotland's World Cup '98 Theme)

Words & Music by Justin Currie

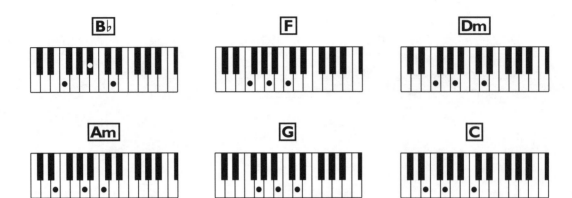

Voice: **Piano**

Rhythm: **Pop Ballad**

Tempo: ♩ = 72

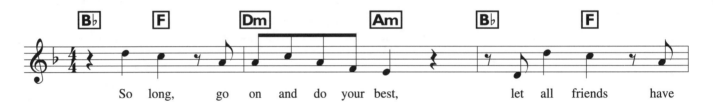

So long, go on and do your best, let all friends have

whis-ky on its prayer. The world may not be sha-ken, yeah, but you might prove them wrong, ev - en

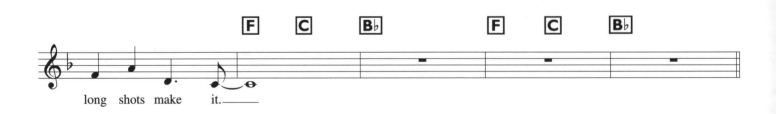

long shots make it.

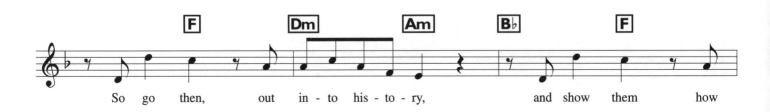

So go then, out in - to his - to - ry, and show them how

ea - sy it can be. And you might not be - lieve it, yeah, but pret - ty soon you'll see, ev - en

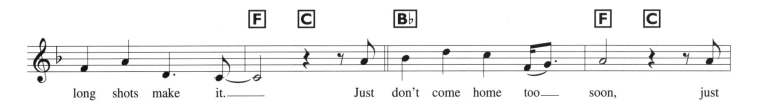

long shots make it.___ Just don't come home too___ soon, just

don't come home too___ soon. I don't

care what peo - ple say, we can laugh it all a - way but if I

have a dream at all, it's that for once you won't be on that stu - pid plane.___

Repeat to fade

And the world may not be sha - ken, yeah, but you might prove them wrong, ev - en

long shots make it.___ Just don't come home too___ soon. Just

GRANDSTAND

By Keith Mansfield

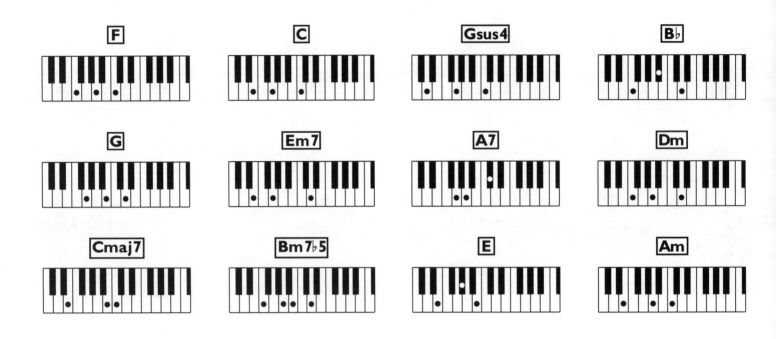

Voice:	**Brass Ensemble**
Rhythm:	**Pop Rock 1**
Tempo:	♩ = 128

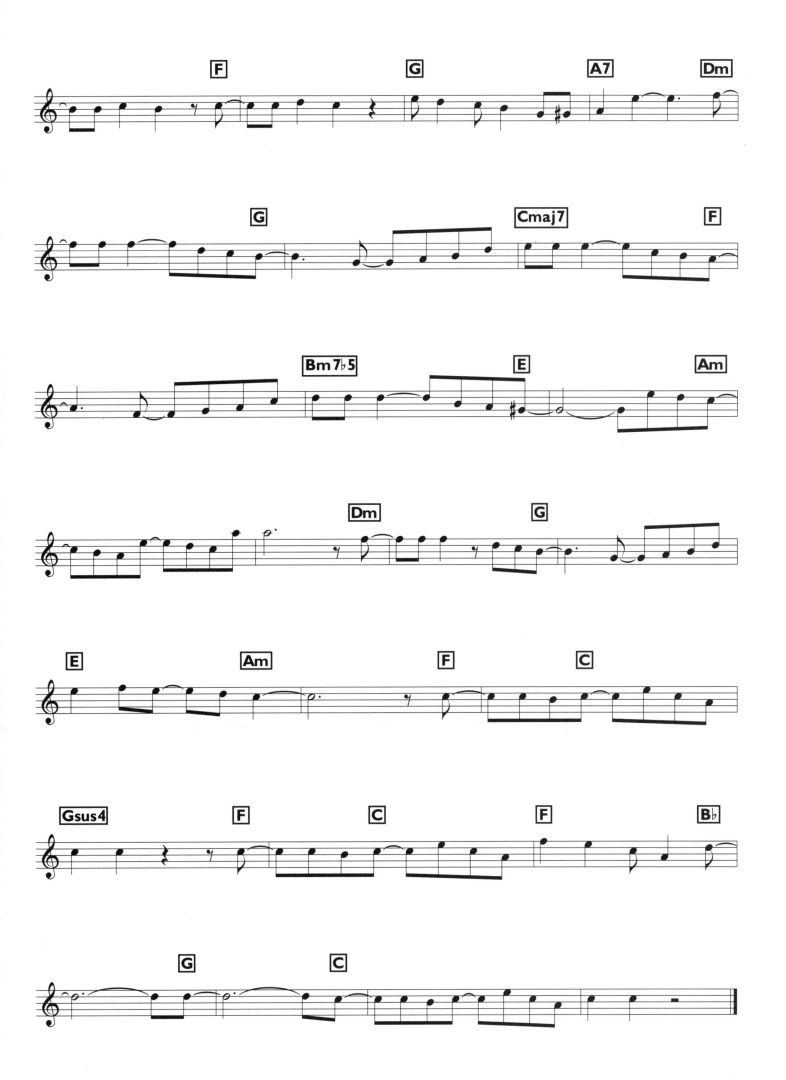

JERUSALEM
(ITV Euro '96)

Music by Hubert Parry
Words by William Blake

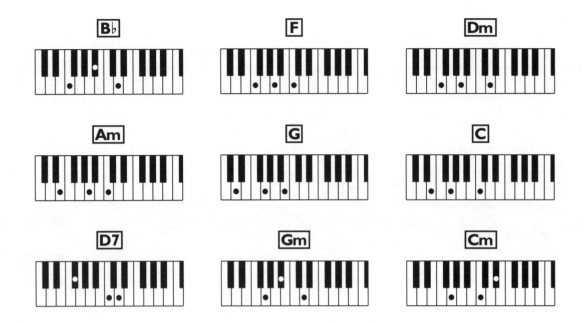

Voice: **Church Organ**

Rhythm: **Waltz**

Tempo: ♩ = 64

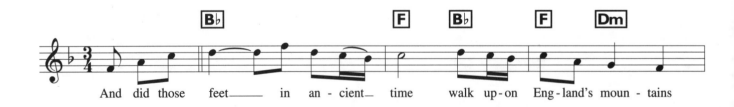

And did those feet—— in an-cient—— time walk up-on Eng-land's moun-tains

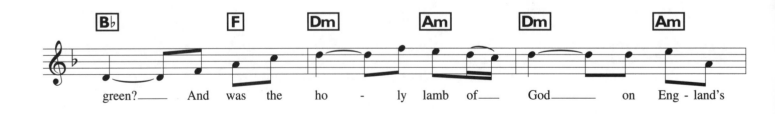

green?—— And was the ho - ly lamb of—— God —— on Eng-land's

plea-sant pas - tures seen?—— And did the coun - te - nance di -

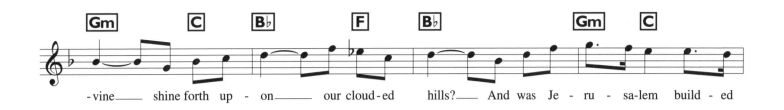

-vine —— shine forth up - on —— our cloud-ed hills? —— And was Je - ru - sa-lem build - ed

here —— a - mong those dark sa-tan - ic hills?

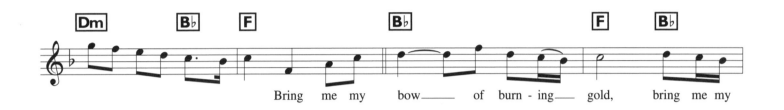

Bring me my bow —— of burn - ing —— gold, bring me my

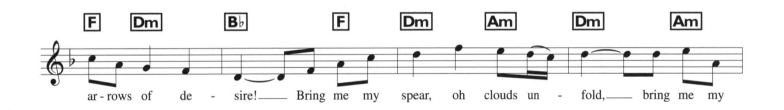

ar - rows of de - sire! —— Bring me my spear, oh clouds un - fold, —— bring me my

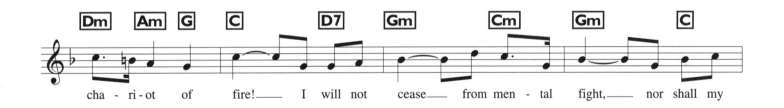

cha - ri - ot of fire! —— I will not cease —— from men - tal fight, —— nor shall my

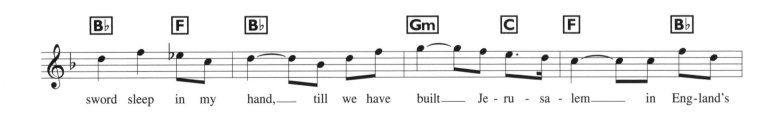

sword sleep in my hand, —— till we have built —— Je - ru - sa - lem —— in Eng-land's

green and plea - sant land.

LA COPA DE LA VIDA
(World Cup '98)

Words & Music by Robi Rosa, Desmond Child & Luis Gomez Escolar
© Copyright 1998 Desmophobia & A Phantom Vox Publishing/Muziekuitgeverij Artemis.
PolyGram Music Publishing Limited, 47 British Grove, London W4 (42%),
Warner Chappell Music Limited, Griffin House, 161 Hammersmith Road, London W6 (42%) &
Musica Calaca, S.L., Alcala 70, 28009 Madrid, Spain (16%).
All Rights Reserved. International Copyright Secured.

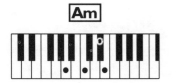
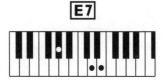
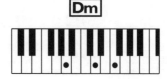
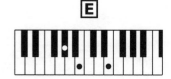

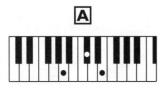
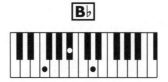
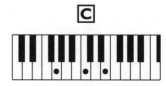

Voice: **Trumpet**

Rhythm: **Samba**

Tempo: ♩ = 120

La vi-da es pu-ra pa-si-ón.___

Hay que lle-nar   Co-pa de a-mor.___   Pa-ra vi-vir   Hay___

___ que lu-char.___   Un co-ra-zón   pa-ra ga-nar.___   Co-mo Ca-

-ín y A-bel___ es un par-ti-do___ cru-él.   Tien-es que pe-lear por un es-

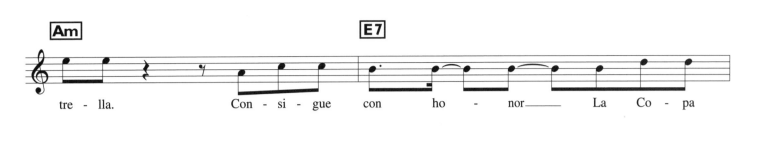

Am ... **E7**

tre - lla. Con - si - gue con ho - nor____ La Co - pa

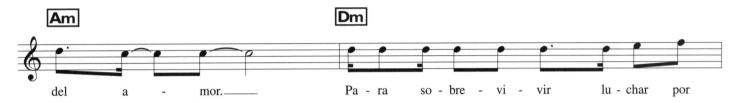

Am ... **Dm**

del a - mor.____ Pa - ra so - bre - vi - vir lu - char por

E **Dm** **E** **Dm** **E**

e - lla. Lu - char por e - lla. Lu - char por e - lla.

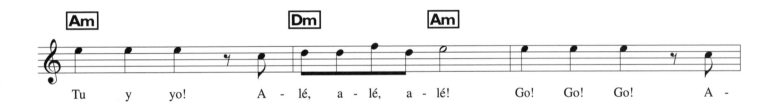

Am **Dm** **Am**

Tu y yo! A - lé, a - lé, a - lé! Go! Go! Go! A -

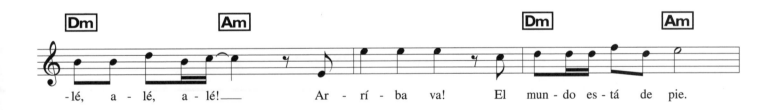

Dm **Am** **Dm** **Am**

-lé, a - lé, a - lé!____ Ar - rí - ba va! El mun - do es - tá de pie.

Dm **Am** **A** **Bb** **C**

Go! Go! Go! A - lé, a - lé, a - lé!____

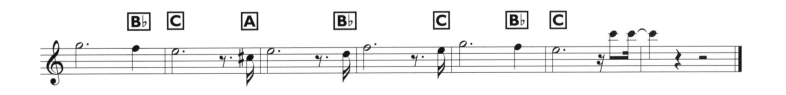

Bb **C** **A** **Bb** **C** **Bb** **C**

LIGHT AND TUNEFUL
(Wimbledon Opening Theme)

By Keith Mansfield

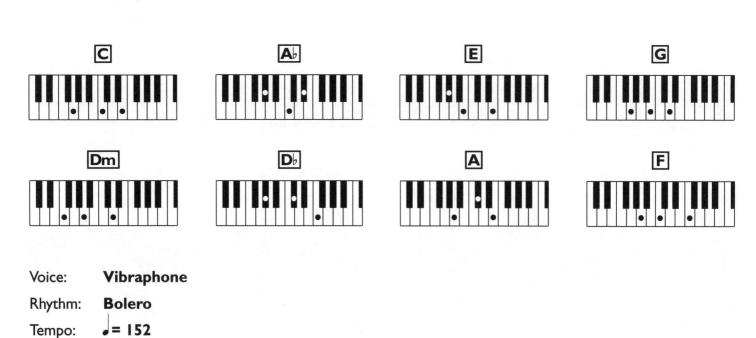

Voice:	**Vibraphone**	
Rhythm:	**Bolero**	
Tempo:	♩ = 152	

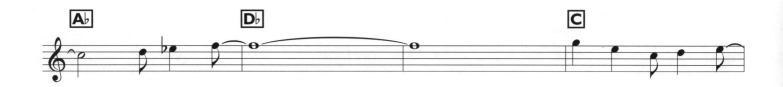

MAS QUE NADA (SAY NO MORE)
(Nike Brazilian Football Airport Advertisement)

Words & Music by Jorge Ben
English Lyric by Norman Gimbel

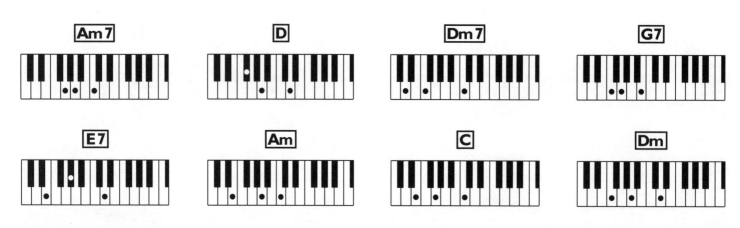

Voice: **Studio Piano**

Rhythm: **Samba**

Tempo: ♩ = 130

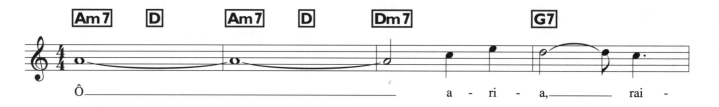

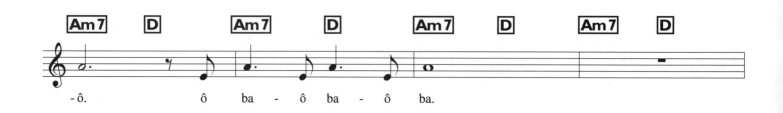

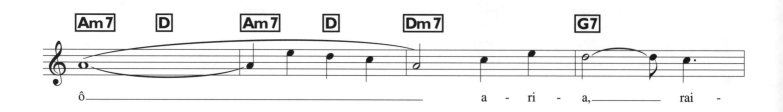

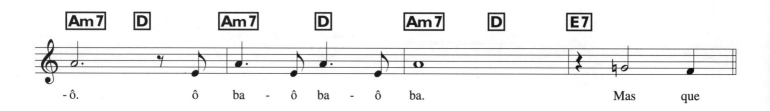

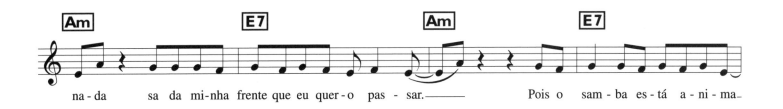

na - da   sa da mi-nha frente que eu quer-o pas - sar._____   Pois o sam-ba es-tá a-ni-ma_

_   do   o que eu quer - o d e___ sam - bar._____   Es - se

sam - ba___ que é mix - to de ma - ra - ca tú._____   é sam-ba de pre-to

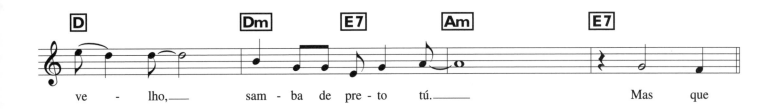

ve - lho,____   sam - ba de pre - to tú._____   Mas que

na - da   um sam-ba co-mo esse tão le-gal,_   vo-cê não vai quer-

-er,   que eu che - gue no___ fi - nal._____   ô

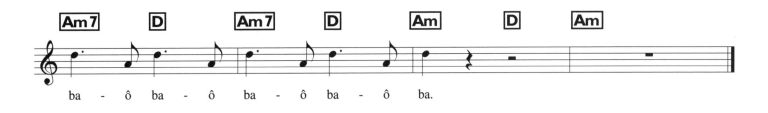

ba - ô ba - ô ba - ô ba - ô ba.

NESSUN DORMA FROM TURANDOT
(BBC World Cup '90)

By Giacomo Puccini

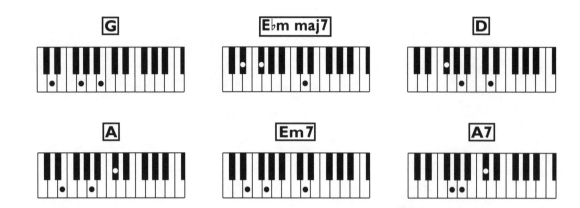

Voice: **Studio Piano**

Rhythm: **Epic Ballad**

Tempo: ♩ = **68**

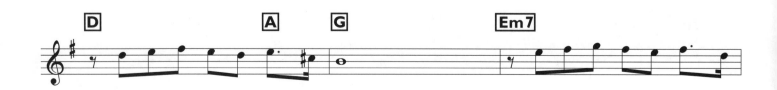

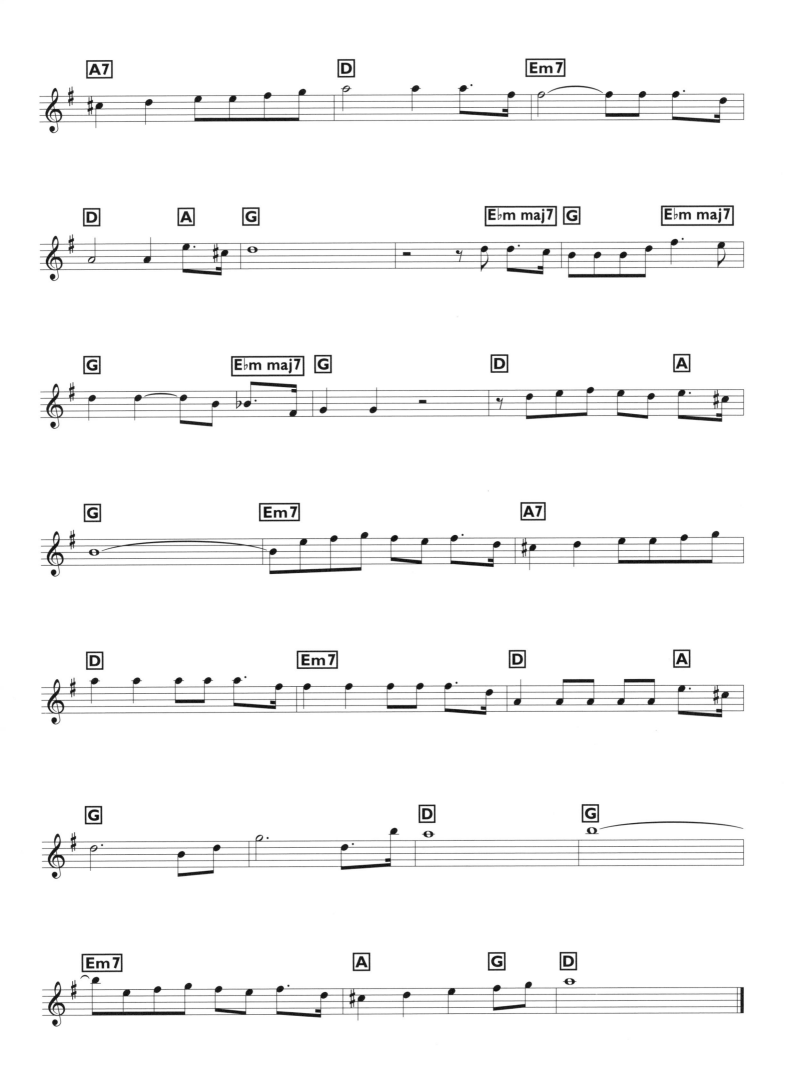

ODE TO JOY FROM SYMPHONY No.9
(BBC Euro '96)

Composed by Ludwig Van Beethoven

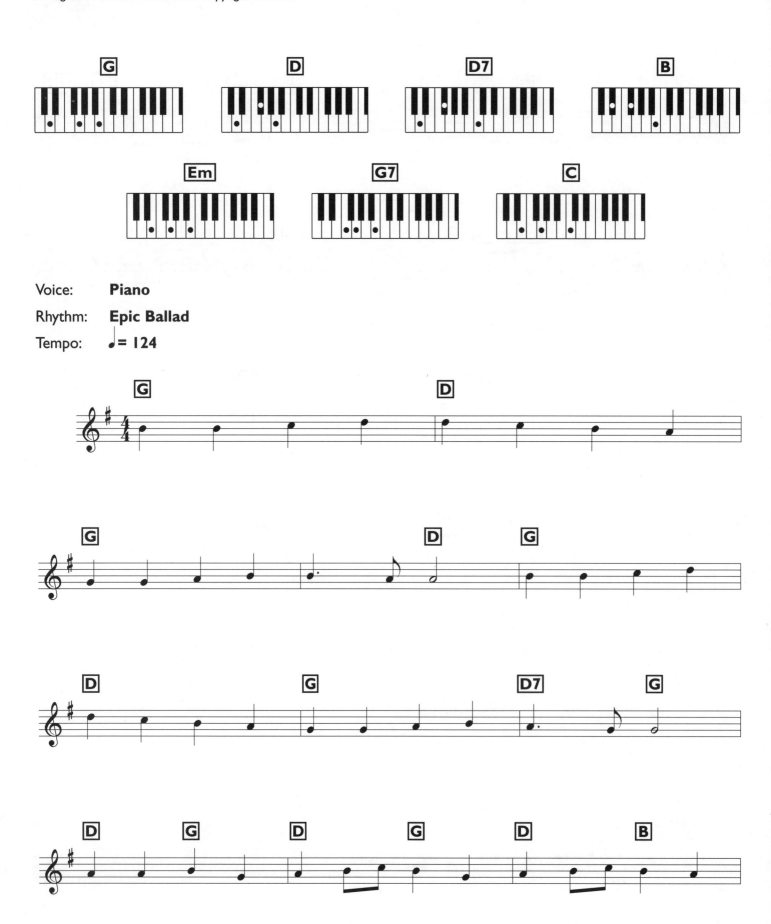

Voice: **Piano**

Rhythm: **Epic Ballad**

Tempo: ♩ = 124

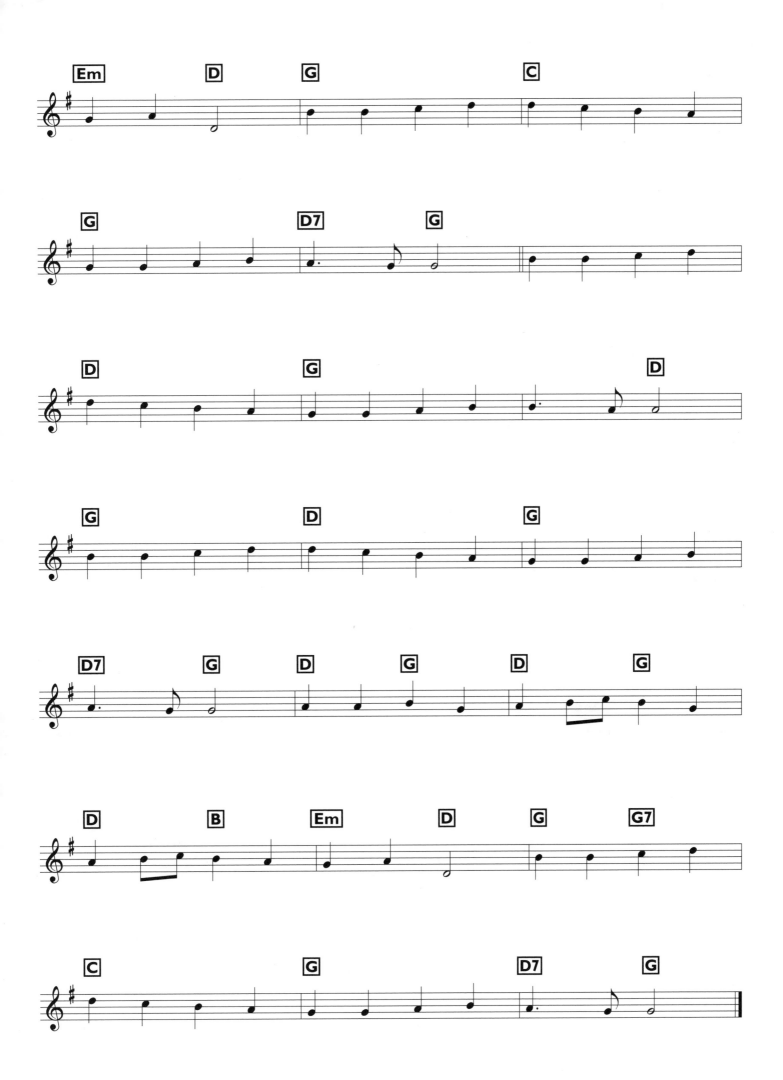

✓PAVANE
(BBC World Cup '98)

Composed by Gabriel Faure, words by Robert de Montesquiou
Arranged by Elizabeth Parker

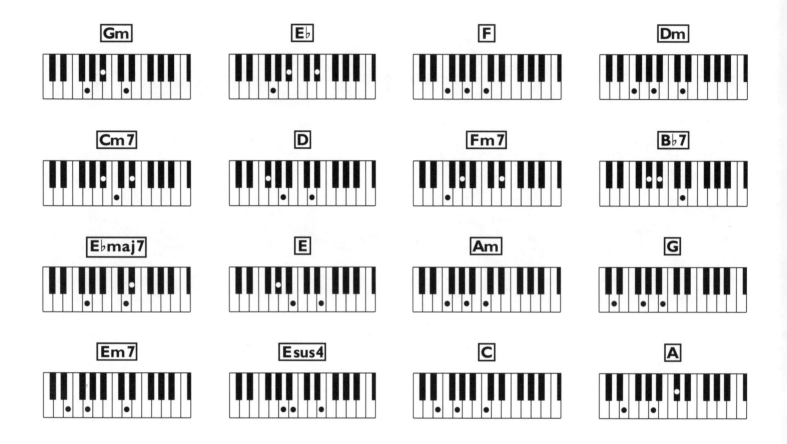

Voice: **Studio Piano**

Rhythm: **Epic Ballad**

Tempo: ♩ = 68

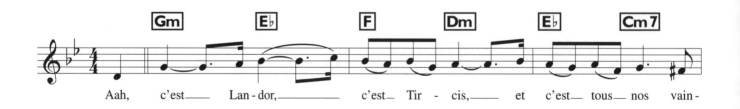

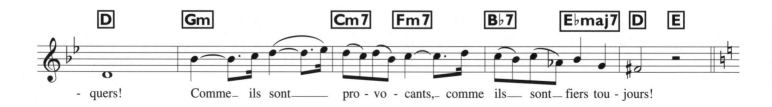

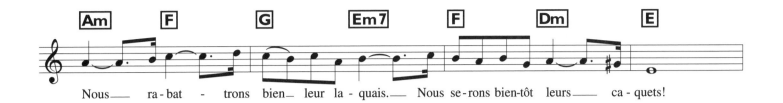

Nous — ra - bat - trons bien leur la - quais. — Nous se - rons bien-tôt leurs — ca - quets!

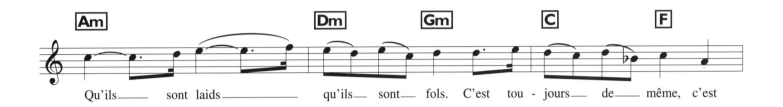

Qu'ils — sont laids — qu'ils — sont — fols. C'est tou - jours — de — même, c'est

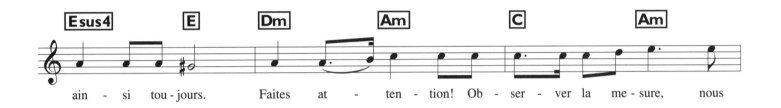

ain - si tou - jours. Faites at - ten - tion! Ob - ser - ver la me - sure, nous

se - rons leurs ca-quets! Qu'ils — sont laids! Et chers — mi-nois! Qu'ils — sont fols!

Airs — co-quets! C'est tou - jours de même, c'est ain - si tou-jours. Aah,

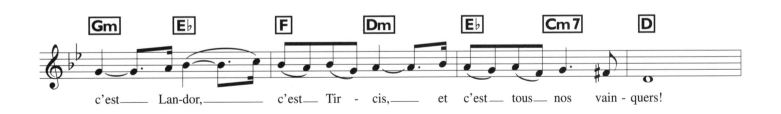

c'est — Lan-dor, — c'est — Tir - cis, — et c'est — tous — nos vain - quers!

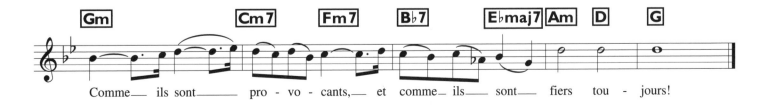

Comme — ils sont — pro - vo - cants, — et comme ils — sont — fiers tou - jours!

POP LOOKS BACH
(Ski Sunday Theme)

By Sam Fonteyn

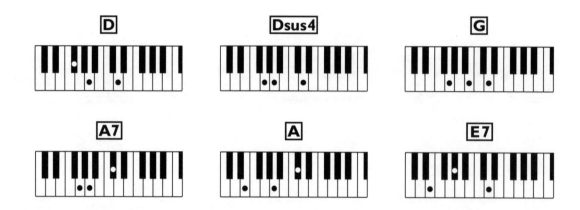

Voice: **Church Organ**

Rhythm: **Pop Rock 1**

Tempo: ♩ = 140

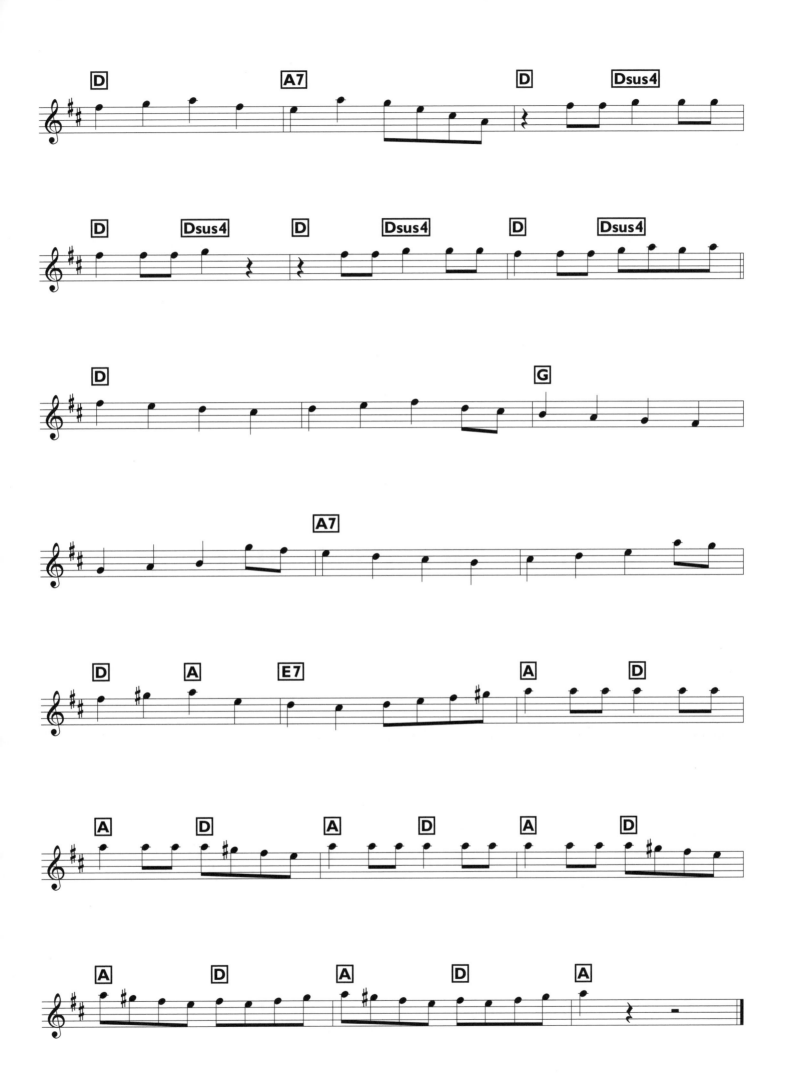

SPORTING OCCASION
(Wimbledon Closing Theme)

By Arnold Steck

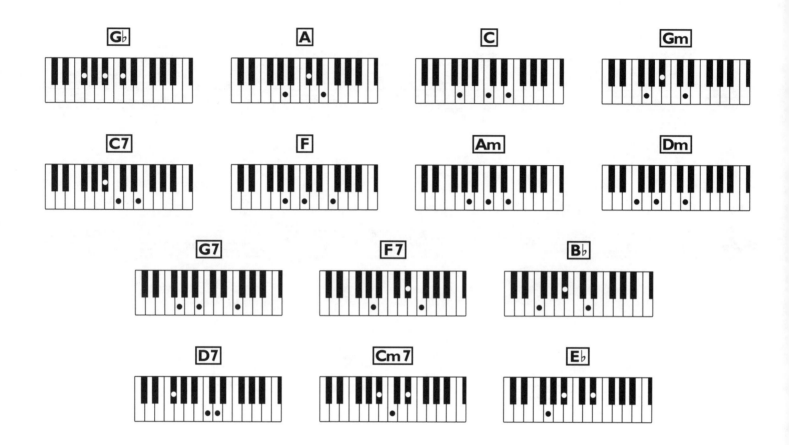

Voice: **Trumpet**

Rhythm: **March 1**

Tempo: ♩ = 122

√SPORTSMASTER

By Robert Busby

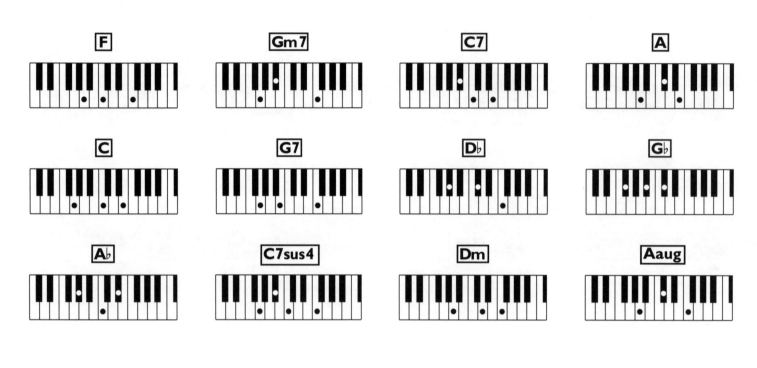

Voice: **Strings 1**

Rhythm: **March 1**

Tempo: ♩ = 120

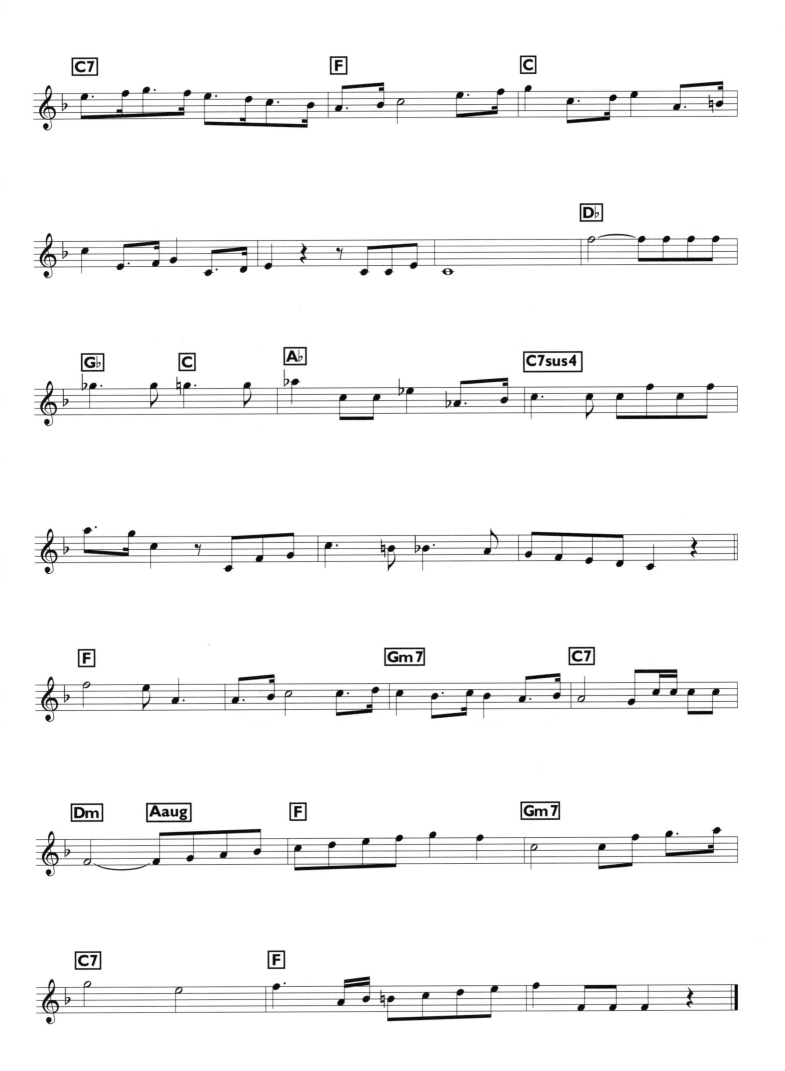

SPORTSNIGHT THEME

By Tony Hatch

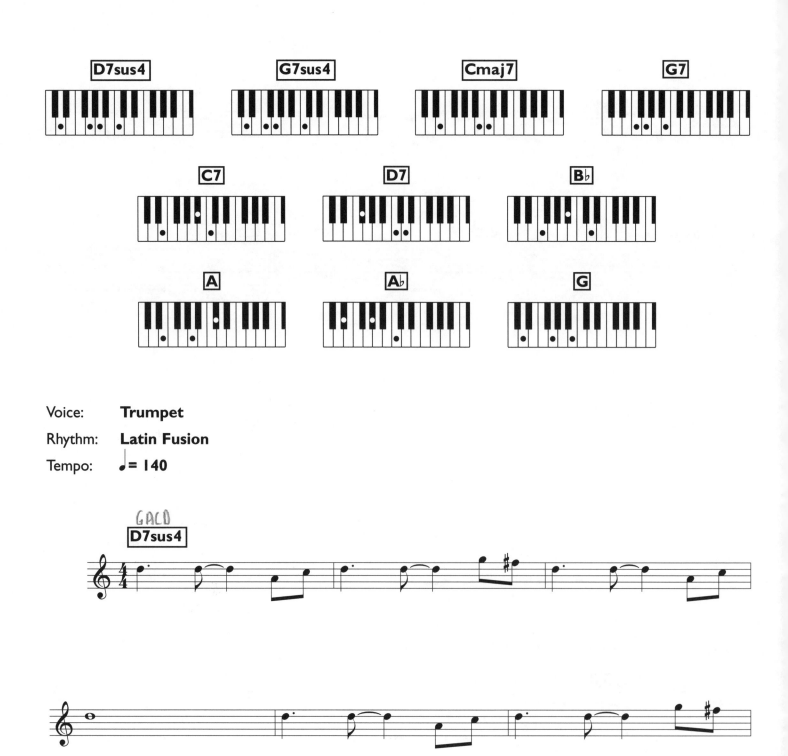

Voice:	**Trumpet**
Rhythm:	**Latin Fusion**
Tempo:	♩ = 140

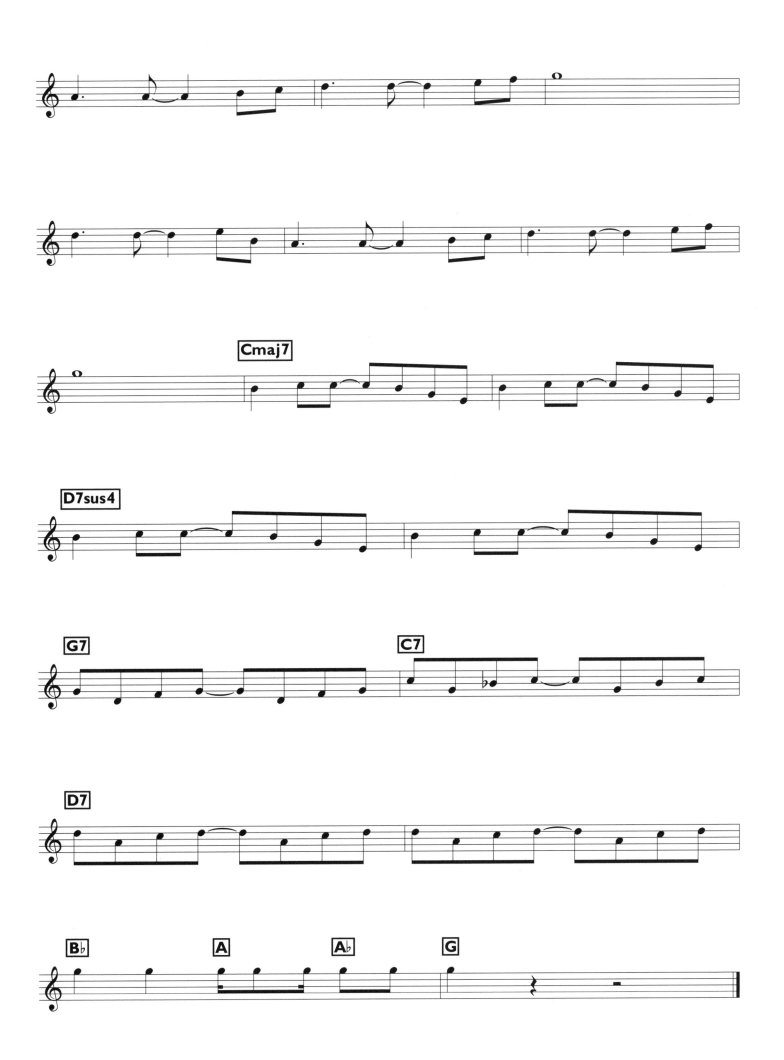

SWING LOW, SWEET CHARIOT
(Rugby Anthem)

Traditional

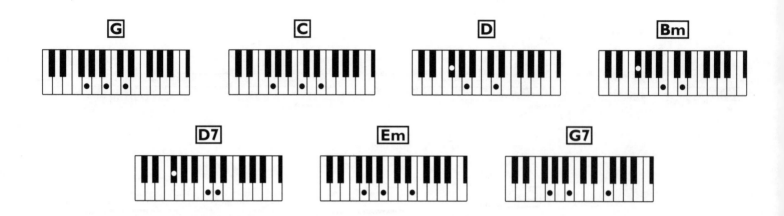

Voice: **Bass/Piano Split**

Rhythm: **Soft Rock 2**

Tempo: ♩ = 108

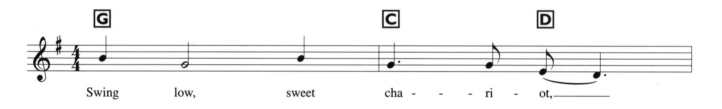

Swing low, sweet cha - - ri - ot,___

com - in' for to car - ry me home,

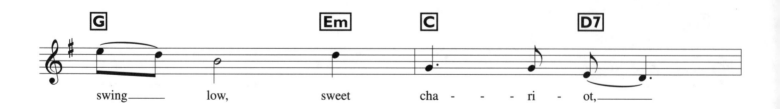

swing___ low, sweet cha - - ri - ot,___

com - in' for to car - ry me home.   I

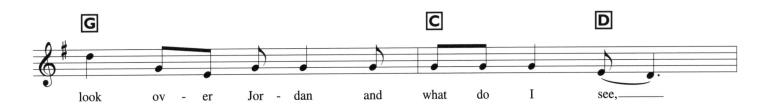

look ov - er Jor - dan and what do I see,_____

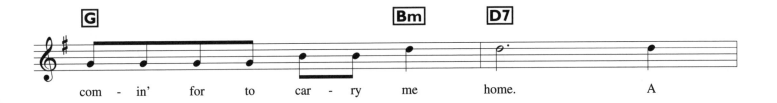

com - in' for to car - ry me home. A

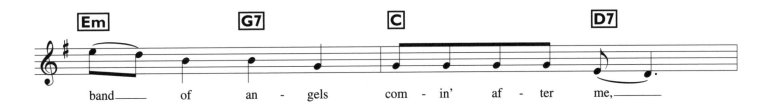

band_____ of an - gels com - in' af - ter me,_____

com - in' for to car - ry me home. Swing low, sweet

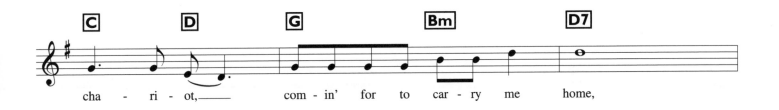

cha - ri - ot,_____ com - in' for to car - ry me home,

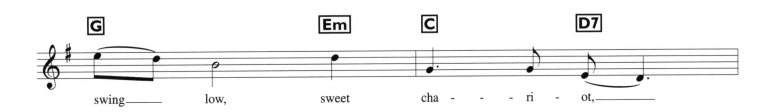

swing_____ low, sweet cha - - ri - ot,_____

com - in' for to car - ry me home.

THE CHAIN
(Grand Prix Theme)

Words & Music by Lindsey Buckingham, John McVie,
Christine McVie, Mick Fleetwood & Stevie Nicks

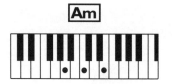
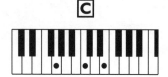

Voice: **Clarinet**

Rhythm: **Pop Rock 2**

Tempo: ♩ = **160**

Repeat to fade

THE TRAP
(London Marathon)

By Ron Goodwin

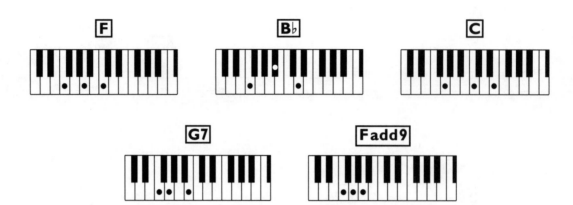

Voice:	**French Horn 1**
Rhythm:	**Waltz**
Tempo:	♩ = 184

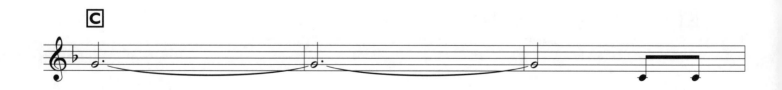

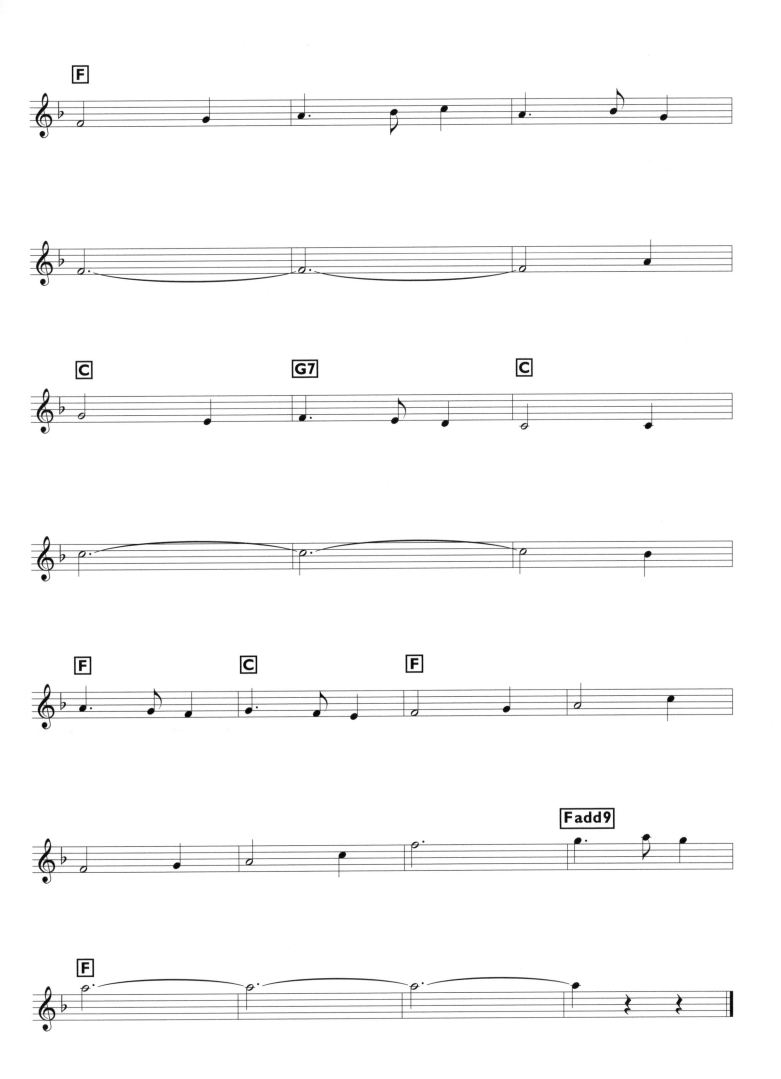

THREE LIONS '98
(World Cup '98)

Music by Ian Broudie
Words by David Baddiel & Frank Skinner

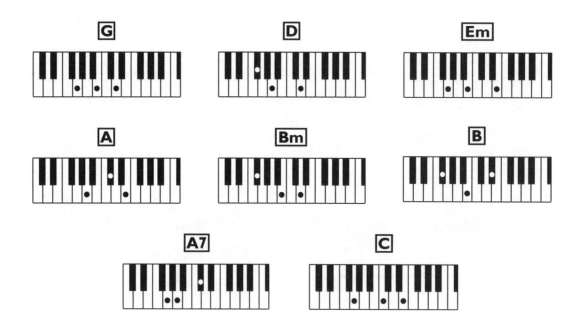

Voice: **Soprano Saxophone**

Rhythm: **Slow Rock 2**

Tempo: ♩ = 126

We still be-lieve,— we still be-lieve,— we still be-lieve,— it's com-ing home,

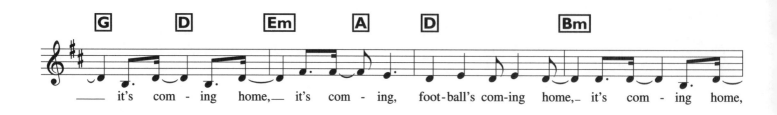

—— it's com-ing home,— it's com-ing, foot-ball's com-ing home,— it's com-ing home,

—— it's com-ing home,— it's com-ing, foot-ball's com-ing home.—

Tears— for he - roes dressed in grey,— no plans for fi - nal

day,———————— stay in bed,— drift a - way,— it could have all been

songs in the street,— it was near - ly com - plete,— it was near - ly so sweet,— and now I'm sing-ing

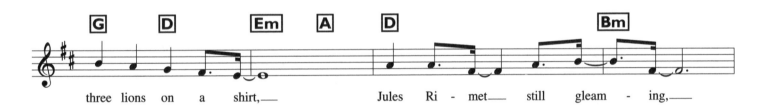

three lions on a shirt,— Jules Ri - met— still gleam - ing,—

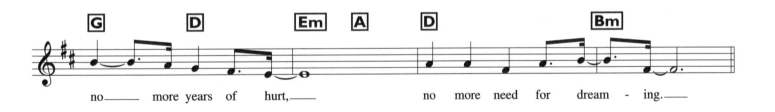

no— more years of hurt,— no more need for dream - ing.—

We can dance Nob-by's dance,— we could dance it in France.———

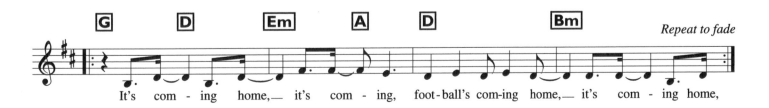

Repeat to fade

It's com - ing home,— it's com - ing, foot-ball's com-ing home,— it's com - ing home,

WORLD IN UNION
(World Cup Rugby 1991)

By Gustav Holst
Arranged by Charlie Skarbek

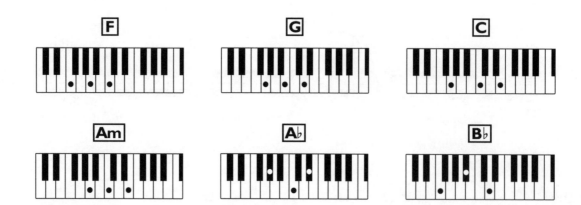

Voice:	**Trumpet**
Rhythm:	**Polka 2**
Tempo:	♩= 88

YOU'LL NEVER WALK ALONE
(Football Anthem)

Music by Richard Rodgers
Words by Oscar Hammerstein II

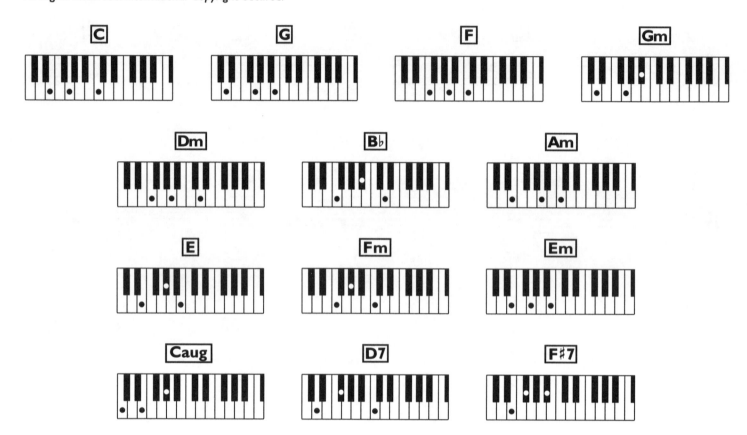

Voice: **Choir/Organ Layer**
Rhythm: **Epic Ballad**
Tempo: ♩ = 108

When you walk through a storm, hold your head up high and

don't be a-fraid of the dark._____ At the

EASIEST KEYBOARD COLLECTION

Easy-to-play melody line arrangements for all keyboards with chord symbols and lyrics. Suggested registration, rhythm and tempo are included for each song together with keyboard diagrams showing left-hand chord voicings used.

  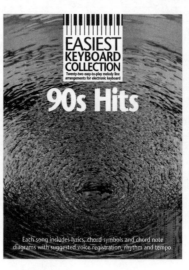 

Showstoppers

Consider Yourself (Oliver!), Do You Hear The People Sing? (Les Misérables), I Know Him So Well (Chess), Maria (West Side Story), Smoke Gets In Your Eyes (Roberta) and 17 more big stage hits.
Order No. AM944218

Pop Classics

A Whiter Shade Of Pale (Procol Harum), Bridge Over Troubled Water (Simon & Garfunkel), Crocodile Rock (Elton John) and nineteen more classic pop hits, including Hey Jude (The Beatles), Imagine (John Lennon), Massachusetts (The Bee Gees) and Stars (Simply Red).
Order No. AM944196

90s Hits

Over twenty of the greatest hits of the 1990s, including Always (Bon Jovi), Fields Of Gold (Sting), Have I Told You Lately (Rod Stewart), One Sweet Day (Mariah Carey), Say You'll Be There (Spice Girls), and Wonderwall (Oasis).
Order No. AM944229

TV Themes

Twenty-two great themes from popular TV series, including Casualty, EastEnders, Gladiators, Heartbeat, I'm Always Here (Baywatch), Red Dwarf and The Black Adder.
Order No. AM944207

Also available...

Ballads, Order No. AM952116 **Film Themes**, Order No. AM952050
Boyzone, Order No. AM958331 **Hits of the 90s**, Order No. AM955780
Broadway, Order No. AM952127 **Jazz Classics**, Order No. AM952061
Chart Hits, Order No. AM952083 **Love Songs**, Order No. AM950708
Christmas, Order No. AM952105 **Pop Hits**, Order No. AM952072
Classic Blues, Order No. AM950697 **60s Hits**, Order No. AM955768
Classical Themes, Order No. AM952094 **80s Hits**, Order No. AM955779